I'm a Little Teapot

I'm a Little Teapot

As told and illustrated by
Iza Trapani

Scholastic Inc.

New York Toronto London Auckland Sydney

A special "thank you" to Emma, Max, and Mick
for their wonderful suggestions.

ISBN 0-590-39961-6

Book and illustrations copyright © 1996 by Whispering Coyote Press L.P.
"I'm A Little Teapot" written by Clarence Kelley and George Sanders
Copyright © 1939 Kelman Music Corporation
Copyright renewed 1967 by Marilyn Sanders O'Bradovich
International copyright secured. All rights reserved.
Adaptation by Iza Trapani © 1996 Marilyn Sanders O'Bradovich
All rights reserved. Published by Scholastic Inc., 555 Broadway,
New York, NY 10012, by arrangement with Whispering Coyote Press.

SCHOLASTIC and associated logos are trademarks and/or registered trademarks
of Scholastic Inc.

24 23 22 21 20 19 18 17 16   0 1 2/0

Printed in the U.S.A.   08

First Scholastic printing, October 1997

Text was set in 18-point Tiffany Medium.

For Jeannie, Laura, and Teri,
"friends forever!"
Love,
Iza

I'm a little teapot, short and stout.
Here is my handle, here is my spout.
When I get all steamed up, hear me shout.
Just tip me over, pour me out!

I'm a little teapot, come see me.
Oh how I'd love your company.
Sitting on the stove top patiently,
I wait for someone to make tea.

I'm a little teapot, I'll show you
All of the things that I'd like to do.
It's a game I play the whole day through.
Now let me share my dreams with you.

I'm a little teapot, on that note
We're off to China—grab your coat.
We can fly a kite and row our boat
And eat with chopsticks as we float.

I'm a little teapot, si señor.
All over Mexico we can tour.
I'll become a mighty matador
And fight the bull while you keep score.

I'm a little teapot, watch me fly
Just like a spaceship in the sky.
On another planet way up high,
We'll meet an alien eye to eye.

I'm a little teapot, la, la, la!
Let's take a trip to the opera.
You can sing a lovely aria,
And I'll play in the orchestra.

I'm a little teapot, hey let's play
Pirates at sea on a windy day.
Back and forth our sailing ship will sway.
Ahoy my mateys! Find the way!

I'm a little teapot, tally ho!
Off on a fox hunt we will go.
Racing with the hounds, our trumpets blow.
Now where on earth did that fox go?

I'm a little teapot, peekaboo!
Deep in the jungle I'll hide with you.
You can try to find me, if you do—
Then you can hide and I'll find you.

I'm a little teapot, golly gee!
Thank you for sharing my dreams with me.
Now I'd really like to make some tea
For all your friends and family.

I'm a little teapot, short and stout.
Here is my handle, here is my spout.
Tip me over gently, pour me out
For that's what tea time's all about!

I'm a Little Teapot

I'm a lit - tle tea - pot, short and stout. Here is my han - dle,

here is my spout. When I get all steamed up,

hear me shout. Just tip me ov - er, and pour me out!

1. I'm a little teapot, short and stout.
   Here is my handle, here is my spout.
   When I get all steamed up, hear me shout.
   Just tip me over, pour me out!

2. I'm a little teapot, come see me.
   Oh how I'd love your company.
   Sitting on the stove top patiently,
   I wait for someone to make tea.

3. I'm a little teapot, I'll show you
   All of the things that I'd like to do.
   It's a game I play the whole day through.
   Now let me share my dreams with you.

4. I'm a little teapot, on that note
   We're off to China—grab your coat.
   We can fly a kite and row our boat
   And eat with chopsticks as we float.

5. I'm a little teapot, si señor.
   All over Mexico we can tour.
   I'll become a mighty matador
   And fight the bull while you keep score.

6. I'm a little teapot, watch me fly
   Just like a spaceship in the sky.
   On another planet way up high,
   We'll meet an alien eye to eye.

7. I'm a little teapot, la, la, la!
   Let's take a trip to the opera.
   You can sing a lovely aria,
   And I'll play in the orchestra.

8. I'm a little teapot, hey let's play
   Pirates at sea on a windy day.
   Back and forth our sailing ship will sway.
   Ahoy my mateys! Find the way!

9. I'm a little teapot, tally ho!
   Off on a fox hunt we will go.
   Racing with the hounds, our trumpets blow.
   Now where on earth did that fox go?

10. I'm a little teapot, peekaboo!
    Deep in the jungle I'll hide with you.
    You can try to find me, if you do—
    Then you can hide and I'll find you.

11. I'm a little teapot, golly gee!
    Thank you for sharing my dreams with me.
    Now I'd really like to make some tea
    For all your friends and family.

12. I'm a little teapot, short and stout.
    Here is my handle, here is my spout.
    Tip me over gently, pour me out
    For that's what tea time's all about!